Make it easy...

Maths

Quick Tests

Age 5-6

Paul Broadbent and Peter Patilla

Test 1 Counting to 10

Use these **numbers** to help you.

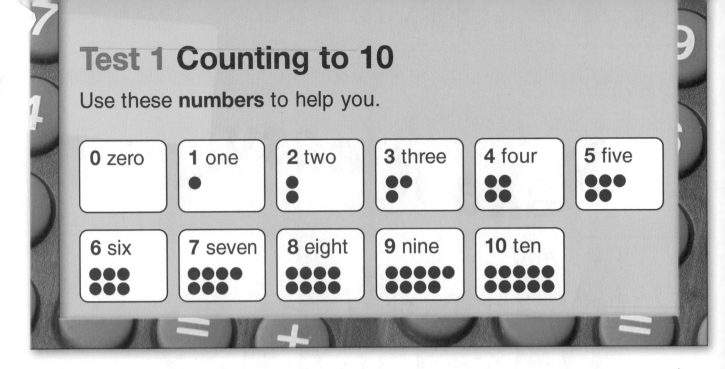

| 0 zero | 1 one | 2 two | 3 three | 4 four | 5 five |
| 6 six | 7 seven | 8 eight | 9 nine | 10 ten |

Count how many marbles. Write the total in the box.

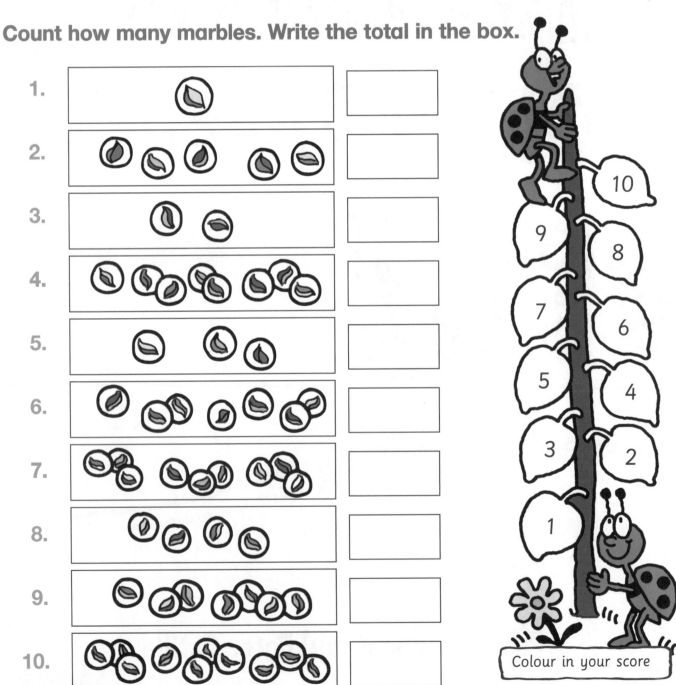

1.

2.

3.

4.

5.

6.

7.

8.

9.

10.

Colour in your score

Test 1

Test 2 Reading and writing numbers to 20

Use these **numbers** and **words** to help you.

0 zero	1 one	2 two	3 three	4 four	5 five
6 six	7 seven	8 eight	9 nine	10 ten	
11 eleven	12 twelve ✓	13 thirteen	14 fourteen	15 fifteen	
16 sixteen	17 seventeen	18 eighteen	19 nineteen	20 twenty	

Write the number.

1. six `6`

2. eight `8`

3. twelve `12`

4. fifteen `15`

5. twenty `20`

Write the word.

6. 3  thirteen

7. 9 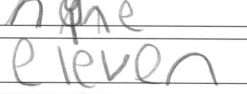 nine

8. 11 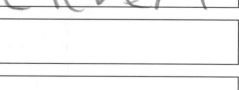 eleven

9. 17

10. 19

10
9
8
7
6
5
4
3
2
1

X

Colour in your score

Test 2

Test 3 Addition to 10

Number lines help you to **add**.

$$3 + 4 = 7$$

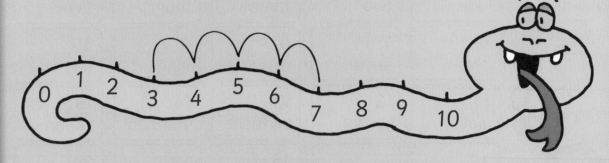

Write the answers to these sums.

1. 6 + 3 =
2. 2 + 5 =
3. 7 + 2 =
4. 4 + 4 =
5. 5 + 4 =
6. 1 + 7 =
7. 5 + 3 =
8. 6 + 4 =
9. 3 + 7 =
10. 8 + 1 =

Colour in your score

Test 3

Test 4 Measures: length

shortest   tallest

Tick the shortest.

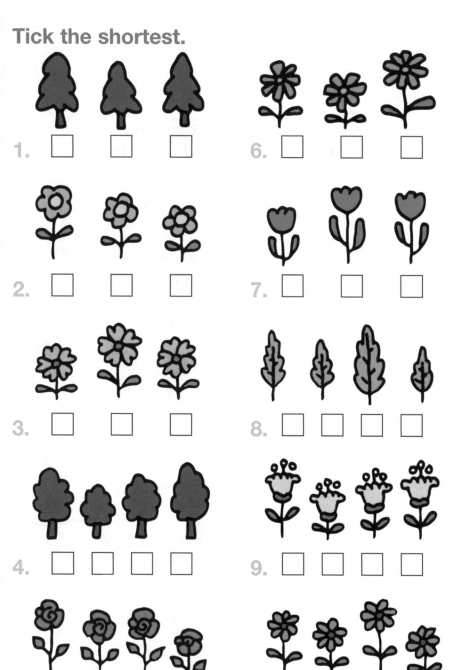

1. ☐ ☐ ☐

2. ☐ ☐ ☐

3. ☐ ☐ ☐

4. ☐ ☐ ☐ ☐

5. ☐ ☐ ☐ ☐

6. ☐ ☐ ☐

7. ☐ ☐ ☐

8. ☐ ☐ ☐ ☐

9. ☐ ☐ ☐ ☐

10. ☐ ☐ ☐ ☐

10
9
8
7
6
5
4
3
2
1

Colour in your score

Test 4

Test 5 2D shapes

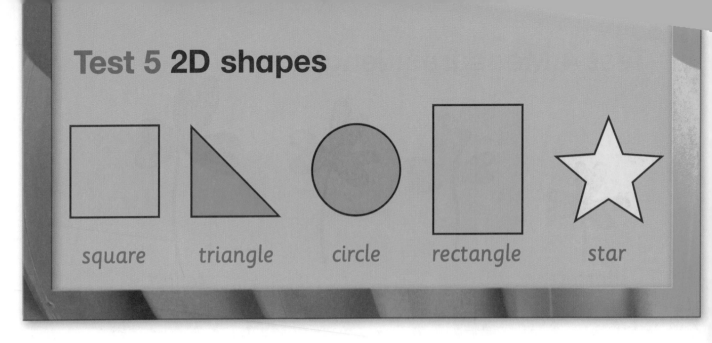

| square | triangle | circle | rectangle | star |

Name each shape.

1. _____

2. _____

3. _____

4. _____

5. _____

Finish drawing each shape.

6. rectangle

7. triangle

8. square

9. star

10. circle

Colour in your score

10
9
8
7
6
5
4
3
2
1

Test 5

Test 6 Counting sequences to 12

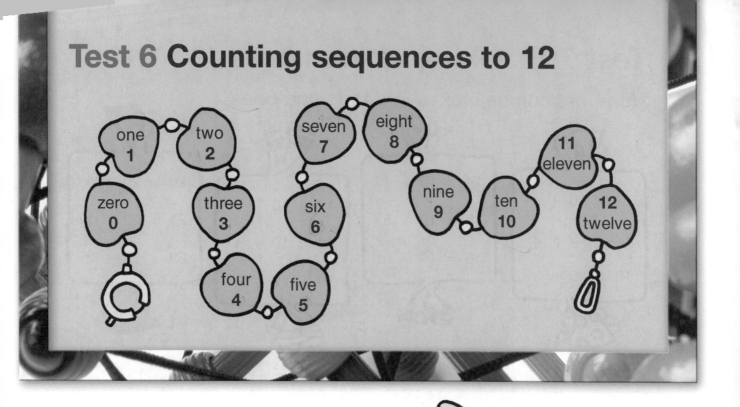

Write the missing numbers.

1. | 2 | 3 | 4 | 5 | 6 |

2. | 5 | 6 | 7 | 8 | 9 |

3. | 7 | 8 | 9 | 10 | 11 |

4. | 9 | 8 | 7 | 6 | 5 |

5. | 6 | 5 | 4 | 3 | 2 |

6. | 8 | 9 | 10 | 11 | 12 |

7. | 3 | 4 | 5 | 6 | 7 |

8. | 12 | 11 | 10 | 9 | 8 |

9. | 8 | 7 | 6 | 5 | 4 |

10. | 10 | 9 | 8 | 7 | 6 |

Colour in your score

Test 6

Test 7 Breaking up numbers

Numbers can be broken into **tens** and **ones**.

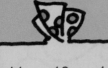

11 = 10 + 1

12 = 10 + 2

13 = 10 + 3

14 = 10 + 4

15 = 10 + 5

16 = 10 + 6

17 = 10 + 7

18 = 10 + 8

19 = 10 + 9

20 = 20 + 0

21 = 20 + 1

22 = 20 + 2

Fill in the missing numbers.

1. 16 = 10 + ☐

2. 14 = 10 + ☐

3. 17 = 10 + ☐

4. 18 = 10 + ☐

5. 21 = 20 + ☐

6. 17 = ☐ + 7

7. 13 = ☐ + 3

8. 12 = ☐ + 2

9. 19 = ☐ + 9

10. 11 = ☐ + 1

Colour in your score

Test 7

Test 8 Adding and subtracting to 20

When **adding**, **count on** from the **larger number**.

9 + 4

0 1 2 3 4 5 6 7 8 9 10 11 12 13 14 15 16 17 18 19 20

When **subtracting**, **count back** from the **larger number**.

12 − 3

0 1 2 3 4 5 6 7 8 9 10 11 12 13 14 15 16 17 18 19 20

Write the answers.

1.   8 + 5 =

2.   2 + 13 =

3.   11 + 4 =

4.   3 + 17 =

5.   15 + 4 =

6.   16 − 3 =

7.   20 − 2 =

8.   18 − 5 =

9.   11 − 2 =

10.   15 − 4 =

Colour in your score

10
9
8
7
6
5
4
3
2
1

Test 8

Test 9 Time: o'clock

The **minute hand** points to **12** for **o'clock times**.

8 o'clock

Write the times.

1.  ☐ o'clock

2.  ☐ o'clock

3.  ☐ o'clock

4.  ☐ o'clock

5.  ☐ o'clock

Draw the missing hand.

6.

six o'clock

7.

four o'clock

8.

eight o'clock

9.

ten o'clock

10.

two o'clock

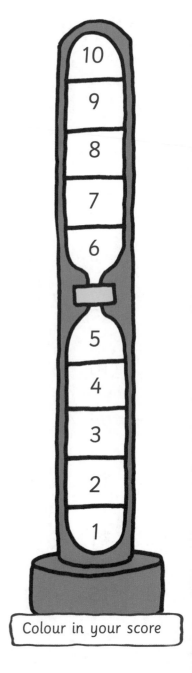

| 10 |
| 9 |
| 8 |
| 7 |
| 6 |
| 5 |
| 4 |
| 3 |
| 2 |
| 1 |

Colour in your score

Test 9

Test 10 Data diagrams

Some diagrams show **opposites**.

square	not square

Draw each shape on the diagram.

1.	2.	3.	4.	5.

straight sides	not straight sides

Write each number on the diagram.

6. 3 7. 11 8. 15 9. 8 10. 10

less than 10	not less than 10

Colour in your score

Test 10

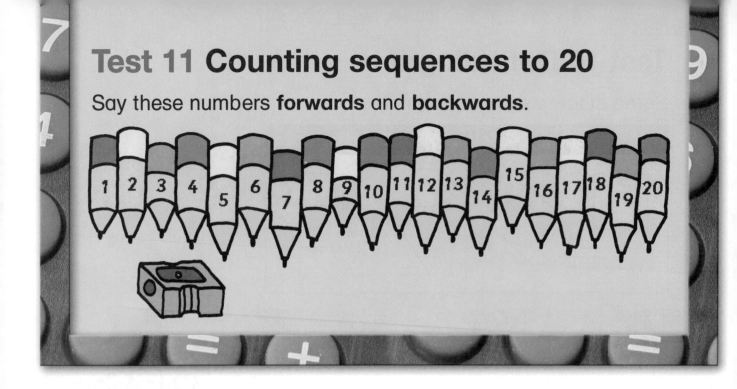

Test 11 Counting sequences to 20

Say these numbers **forwards** and **backwards**.

Write the missing numbers.

1.  8 9 10

2.  10 11 12

3.  15 16 17

4.  15 14 13

5.  10 9 8

6.  14 15 16

7.  8 9 10

8.  20 19 18

9.  16 15 14

10.  19 17 15

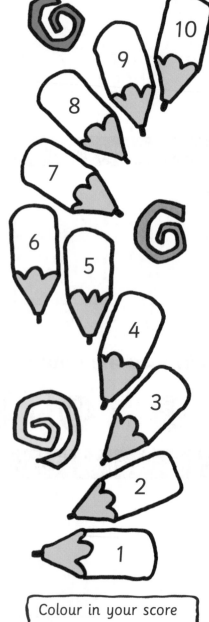

Colour in your score

Test 11

Test 12 Ordinal numbers

Some numbers show the **order** of things.

1. Colour the 3rd snail.

2. Colour the 1st star.

3. Colour the 4th spider.

4. Colour the 2nd ladybird.

5. Colour the last worm.

6. Colour the 3rd letter.

PETER

7. Colour the 4th letter.

PAUL

8. Colour the 5th letter.

SALLY

9. Colour the 2nd letter.

HARRY

10. Colour the last letter.

GITA

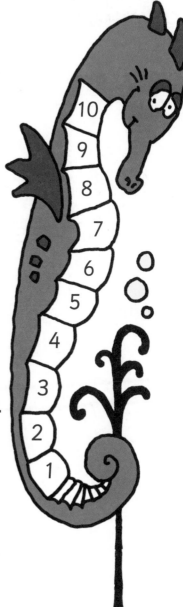

Colour in your score

Test 12

Test 13 Subtraction within 10

Jumping **back** is the same as **subtraction**.

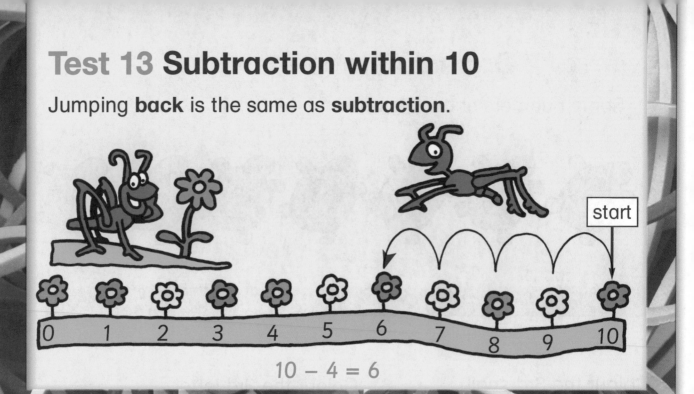

$$10 - 4 = 6$$

Use the number line to help answer these.

1.   7 – 2 =

2.   8 – 4 =

3.   5 – 5 =

4.   9 – 1 =

5.   8 – 6 =

6.   7 – 5 =

7.   10 – 8 =

8.   6 – 4 =

9.   10 – 5 =

10.   9 – 3 =

Colour in your score

Test 13

Test 14 Measures: weight

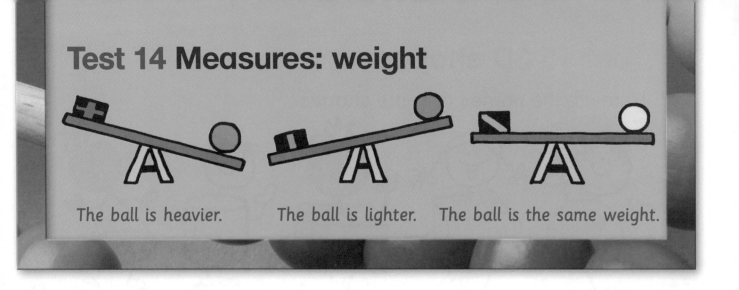

The ball is heavier. The ball is lighter. The ball is the same weight.

Underline the word to show whether the ball is heavier, lighter or the same weight.

1. heavier lighter same

2. heavier lighter same

3. heavier lighter same

4. heavier lighter same

5. heavier lighter same

6. heavier lighter same

7. heavier lighter same

8. heavier lighter same

9. heavier lighter same

10. heavier lighter same

Colour in your score

Test 14

Test 15 3D shapes

Here are the **names** of some **shapes**.

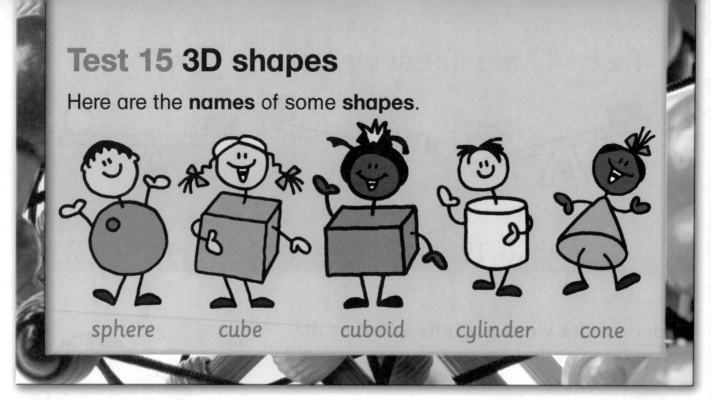

sphere　　　cube　　　cuboid　　　cylinder　　　cone

Join each shape to its name.

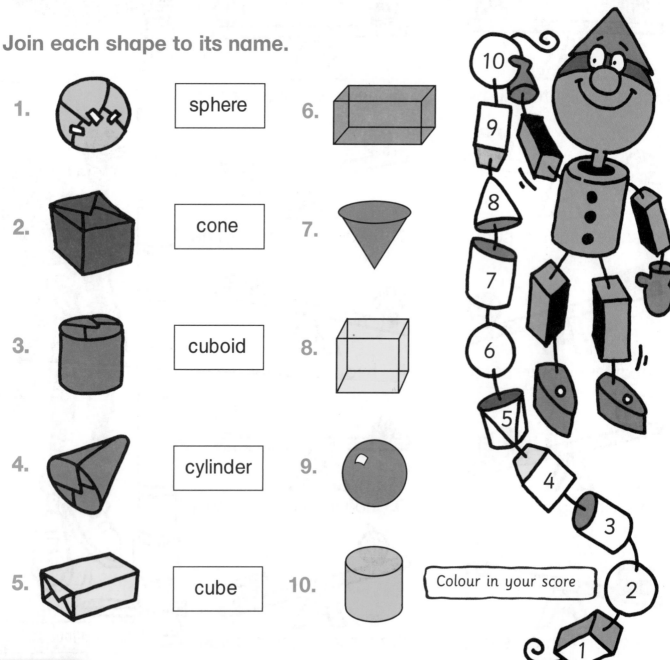

1.

sphere

2.

cone

3.

cuboid

4.

cylinder

5.

cube

6.

7.

8.

9.

10.

Colour in your score

10
9
8
7
6
5
4
3
2
1

Test 16 Counting on and back

It is very useful to be able to **count on** and **back**.

count on 3   count back 3

Write these missing numbers.

1. 4 | count on 6 → ☐

2. 3 | count on 5 → ☐

3. 7 | count on 8 → ☐

4. 12 | count back 2 → ☐

5. 17 | count back 5 → ☐

count on
6. (7) ☐ (12)

count on
7. (9) ☐ (15)

count back
8. (12) ☐ (8)

count back
9. (13) ☐ (6)

count back
10. (20) ☐ (13)

Colour in your score

Test 17 Comparing numbers

13 is bigger than **9**   **6** is smaller than **12**

numbers this way are getting smaller

numbers this way are getting bigger

5 6 7 8 9 10 11 12 13 14 15 16

Colour the bigger number.   **Colour the smaller number.**

1. (12) (7)   6. (4) (7)

2. (11) (14)   7. (11) (19)

3. (15) (12)   8. (13) (12)

4. (10) (11)   9. (15) (8)

5. (13) (16)   10. (13) (17)

10
9
8
7
6
5
4
3
2
1

Colour in your score

Test 17

Test 18 Addition using doubles

Near doubles can help us add.

$2 + 2 = 4$

$2 + 3 = 5$

Add these doubles.

1.  • | • = ☐

2. ⋰ | ⋰ = ☐

3. ∷ | ∷ = ☐

4. ⋮⋮ | ⋮⋮ = ☐

5. ⁙ | ⁙ = ☐

Add these near doubles.

6. | 4 | 3 | = ☐

7. | 2 | 3 | = ☐

8. | 5 | 6 | = ☐

9. | 4 | 3 | = ☐

10. | 4 | 5 | = ☐

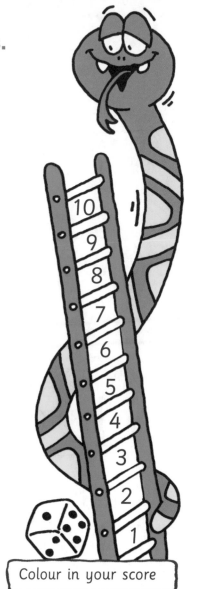

Colour in your score

Test 18

Test 19 Time: half past

The **minute hand** points to **6** for **half past** times.

half past 8

Write the times.

1. half past ☐

2.  half past ☐

3.  half past ☐

4.  half past ☐

5.  half past ☐

Draw the missing hand.

6. half past 1

7.  half past 11

8.  half past 4

9.  half past 7

10.  half past 9

Colour in your score

Test 19

Test 20 Data graphs

This **graph** shows children's favourite ice-creams.

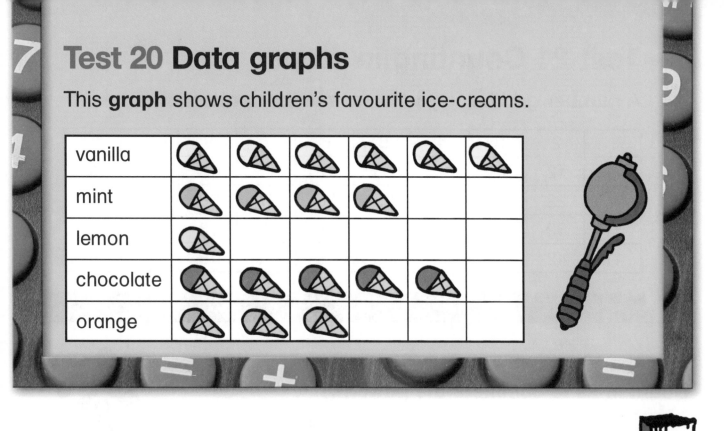

vanilla	🍦	🍦	🍦	🍦	🍦	🍦
mint	🍦	🍦	🍦	🍦		
lemon	🍦					
chocolate	🍦	🍦	🍦	🍦	🍦	
orange	🍦	🍦	🍦			

How many children's favourite was:

1. chocolate?

2. mint?

3. vanilla?

4. orange?

5. lemon?

6. Which was the favourite?

7. Which was the least favourite?

8. Which was chosen by 4 children?

9. Which was chosen by 3 children?

10. How many children were there altogether?

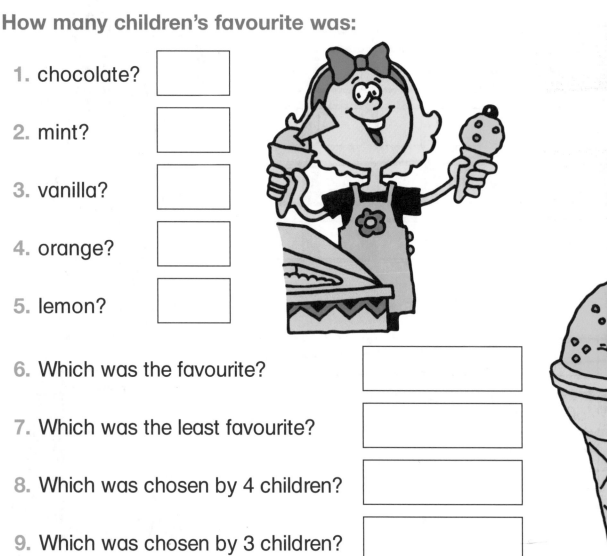

Colour in your score

Test 20

Test 21 Counting in steps

A **number grid** helps you to see **number patterns**.

1	2	3	4	5	6	7	8	9	10
11	12	13	14	15	16	17	18	19	20
21	22	23	24	25	26	27	28	29	30
31	32	33	34	35	36	37	38	39	40
41	42	43	44	45	46	47	48	49	50

Count in 2s to complete the pattern.

1. | 4 | 6 | 8 | | | |

2. | 30 | 28 | 26 | | | |

3. | 3 | 5 | 7 | | | |

4. | 15 | 17 | 19 | | | |

5. | 21 | 19 | 17 | | | |

Count in 5s to complete the pattern.

6. | 5 | 10 | 15 | | | |

7. | 50 | 45 | 40 | | | |

8. | 1 | 6 | 11 | | | |

9. | 2 | 7 | 12 | | | |

10. | 30 | 25 | 20 | | | |

Colour in your score

Test 21

Test 22 More or less

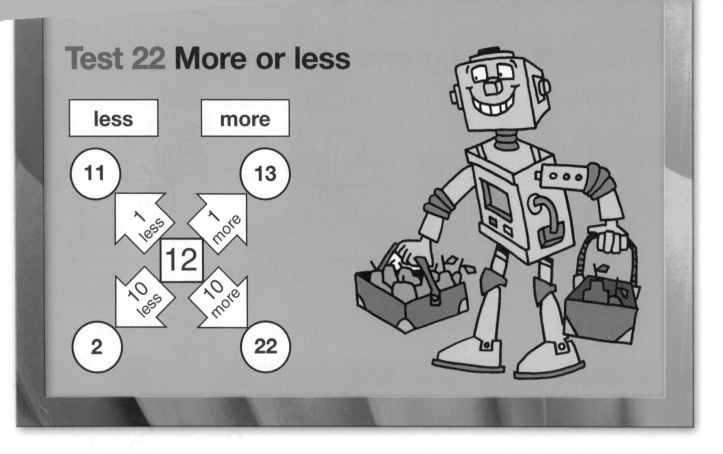

less	more
11	13

1 less · 1 more
12
10 less · 10 more

2 · 22

Make less.

1. 17 → 1 less → ◯

2. 21 → 1 less → ◯

3. 25 → 10 less → ◯

4. 31 → 10 less → ◯

5. 35 → 10 less → ◯

Make more.

6. 5 → 1 more → ◯

7. 8 → 1 more → ◯

8. 6 → 10 more → ◯

9. 11 → 10 more → ◯

10. 15 → 10 more → ◯

Colour in your score

Test 23 Adding and subtracting

A **number line** will help with **adding** and **subtracting**.

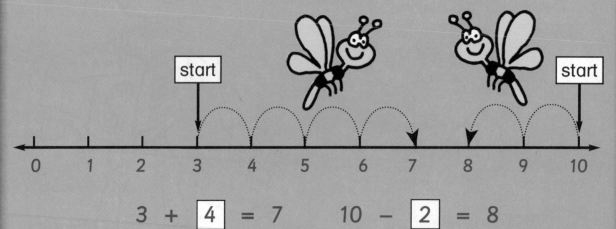

$$3 + \boxed{4} = 7 \qquad 10 - \boxed{2} = 8$$

Write the missing number in the box.

1. $3 + \boxed{} = 10$

2. $2 + \boxed{} = 7$

3. $7 + \boxed{} = 10$

4. $4 + \boxed{} = 8$

5. $3 + \boxed{} = 9$

6. $8 - \boxed{} = 4$

7. $7 - \boxed{} = 1$

8. $5 - \boxed{} = 2$

9. $9 - \boxed{} = 6$

10. $4 - \boxed{} = 0$

Colour in your score

Test 23

Test 24 Measures: capacity

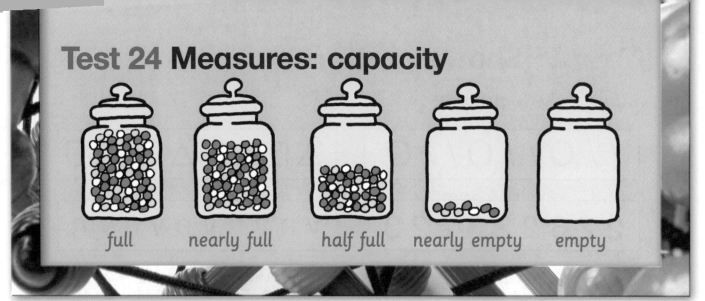

full   nearly full   half full   nearly empty   empty

Colour the mugs and bowls to show how full they are.

1. half full

2. empty

3. nearly full

4. nearly empty

5. full

6. full

7. nearly empty

8. empty

9. nearly full

10. half full

Colour in your score

Test 24

Test 25 Shapes patterns

Look at these **patterns**.

// O // O // O	△□△□△□△□
2 2 3 2 2 3 2 2 3	v n v n v n v n v n

Continue each pattern.

1.

2.

3.

4.

5.

6. 1 1 2 1 1 2

7. |o|o|o|

8. □□•□□•

9. △□•△□•

10. 1 2 3 1 2 3

10
9
8
7
6
5
4
3
2
1

Colour in your score

Test 25

Test 26 Odds and evens

even numbers					odd numbers				
2	4	6	8	10	1	3	5	7	9
These end in 2, 4, 6, 8, or 0.					These end in 1, 3, 5, 7, or 9.				

Write the next odd number.

Write the next even number.

1. (3) ➡ ( )

6. [4] ➡ [ ]

2. (7) ➡ ( )

7. [8] ➡ [ ]

3. (11) ➡ ( )

8. [12] ➡ [ ]

4. (15) ➡ ( )

9. [16] ➡ [ ]

5. (19) ➡ ( )

10. [20] ➡ [ ]

10
9
8
7
6
5
4
3
2
1

Colour in your score

Test 27 Ordering numbers

Number tracks help us to put numbers in **order**.

Write these numbers in order.

1. | 8 | 1 | 4 | 2 | 6 | ➡ | 1 | | | |

2. | 3 | 4 | 7 | 9 | 2 | ➡ | 2 | | | |

3. | 10 | 2 | 9 | 6 | 4 | ➡ | 2 | | | |

4. | 10 | 3 | 15 | 5 | 7 | ➡ | 3 | | | |

5. | 5 | 11 | 8 | 17 | 9 | ➡ | 5 | | | |

6. | 15 | 10 | 17 | 9 | 20 | ➡ | 9 | | | |

7. | 11 | 19 | 10 | 14 | 12 | ➡ | 10 | | | |

8. | 11 | 17 | 13 | 12 | 19 | ➡ | 11 | | | |

9. | 14 | 16 | 13 | 20 | 15 | ➡ | 13 | | | |

10. | 17 | 16 | 20 | 18 | 19 | ➡ | 16 | | | |

Colour in your score

Test 27

Test 28 Addition patterns

Addition facts to **10** are important.

10 + 0	9 + 1	8 + 2	7 + 3	6 + 4	5 + 5
0 + 10	1 + 9	2 + 8	3 + 7	4 + 6	

10

Write the missing number in the box.

1. 7 + ☐ = 10

2. 4 + ☐ = 10

3. 8 + ☐ = 10

4. 3 + ☐ = 10

5. 9 + ☐ = 10

6. ☐ + 1 = 10

7. ☐ + 4 = 10

8. ☐ + 6 = 10

9. ☐ + 8 = 10

10. ☐ + 3 = 10

Colour in your score

Test 28

Test 29 Days of the week

Learn the **order** of the **days**.

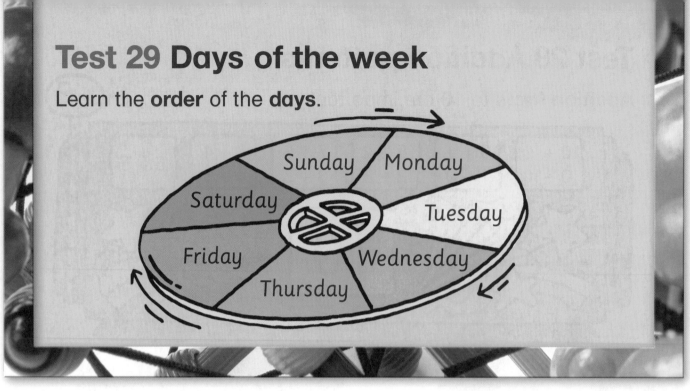

Write the day before:

1. Monday

2. Thursday

3. Wednesday

4. Tuesday

5. Saturday

Write the day after:

6. Friday

7. Sunday

8. Tuesday

9. Saturday

10. Wednesday

Colour in your score

Test 29

Test 30 Learning to tally

Tally marks show how **many**.

1	2	3	4	5
I	II	III	IIII	IIII̷

6	7	8	9	10
IIII̷ I	IIII̷ II	IIII̷ III	IIII̷ IIII	IIII̷ IIII̷

Make tally marks to show how many fish and insects there are.

1.

2.

3.

4.

5.

6.

7.

8.

9.

10.

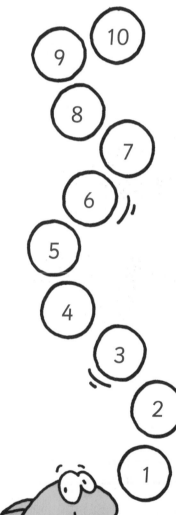

Colour in your score

Test 30

ANSWERS

Test 1
1. 1
2. 5
3. 2
4. 8
5. 3
6. 7
7. 9
8. 4
9. 7
10. 10

Test 2
1. 6
2. 8
3. 12
4. 15
5. 20
6. three
7. nine
8. eleven
9. seventeen
10. nineteen

Test 3
1. 9
2. 7
3. 9
4. 8
5. 9
6. 8
7. 8
8. 10
9. 10
10. 9

Test 4
1. ☐ ☑ ☐
2. ☐ ☐ ☑
3. ☑ ☐ ☐
4. ☐ ☑ ☐ ☐
5. ☐ ☐ ☐ ☑
6. ☐ ☑ ☐
7. ☑ ☐ ☐
8. ☐ ☐ ☐ ☑
9. ☐ ☑ ☐ ☐
10. ☐ ☐ ☐ ☑

Test 5
1. square
2. rectangle
3. triangle
4. star
5. circle

6. ☐ (square)
7. △ (triangle)
8. ☐ (square)
9. ☆ (star)
10. ◯ (circle)

Test 6
The missing numbers are in **bold**.
1. 2 3 4 **5 6**
2. **5 6** 7 8 9
3. **7 8** 9 10 **11**
4. 9 8 7 **6 5**
5. **6 5** 4 3 **2**
6. **8 9** 10 11 12
7. **3** 4 5 **6 7**
8. 12 11 10 **9 8**
9. **8 7** 6 5 4
10. **10 9** 8 7 6

Test 7
1. 6
2. 4
3. 7
4. 8
5. 1
6. 10
7. 10
8. 10
9. 10
10. 10

Test 8
1. 13
2. 15
3. 15
4. 20
5. 19
6. 13
7. 18
8. 13
9. 9
10. 11

Test 9
1. 3 o'clock
2. 9 o'clock
3. 1 o'clock
4. 10 o'clock
5. 5 o'clock

6. clock
7. clock
8. clock
9. clock
10. clock

Test 10
1. straight sides
2. not straight sides
3. straight sides
4. not straight sides
5. straight sides
6. less than 10
7. not less than 10
8. not less than 10
9. less than 10
10. not less than 10

Test 11
The missing numbers are in **bold**.
1. 8 9 10 **11 12 13**
2. **8 9** 10 11 12 **13**
3. **14** 15 16 17 **18 19**
4. 15 14 13 **12 11 10**
5. **12 11** 10 9 8 7
6. 14 15 16 **17 18 19**
7. **7** 8 9 10 **11 12**
8. 20 19 18 **17 16 15**
9. **17** 16 15 14 **13 12**
10. 19 **18** 17 **16** 15 14

Test 12
1. (4 snails)
2. (4 stars)
3. (4 spiders)
4. (4 ladybirds)
5. (5 snails)
6. T
7. L
8. Y
9. A
10. A

Test 13
1. 5
2. 4
3. 0
4. 8
5. 2
6. 2
7. 2
8. 2
9. 5
10. 6

Test 14
1. same
2. heavier
3. heavier
4. lighter
5. lighter
6. same
7. lighter
8. heavier
9. same
10. lighter

Test 15
1. sphere
2. cube
3. cylinder
4. cone
5. cuboid
6. cuboid
7. cone
8. cube
9. sphere
10. cylinder

Test 16
1. 10
2. 8
3. 15
4. 10
5. 12
6. 5
7. 6
8. 4
9. 7
10. 7